Tree-
HOUSE
Comix
Proudly
Presents

DOG MAN
LORD OF THE FLEAS

WRITTEN AND ILLUSTRATED BY **DAV PILKEY**

AS GEORGE BEARD AND HAROLD HUTCHINS

WITH COLOR BY JOSE GARIBALDI

graphix

AN IMPRINT OF

SCHOLASTIC

THANK YOU TO A DEAR FRIEND, RACHEL "RAY RAY" COUN, WHO WAS THERE FROM THE START

Copyright © 2018 by Dav Pilkey
www.pilkey.com

All rights reserved. Published by Graphix, an imprint of Scholastic Inc., Publishers since 1920. SCHOLASTIC, GRAPHIX, and associated logos are trademarks and/or registered trademarks of Scholastic Inc. DOG MAN and related designs, TREE HOUSE COMIX and related designs, and CAPTAIN UNDERPANTS and related designs are trademarks and/or registered trademarks of Dav Pilkey.

Library of Congress Control Number 2017963497

978-0-545-93517-3 (POB)
978-1-338-29091-2 (Library)

10 9 8 7 6 5 4 3 2 1   18 19 20 21 22

Printed in China   62
First edition, September 2018

Edited by Anamika Bhatnagar
Book design by Dav Pilkey and Phil Falco
Color by Jose Garibaldi
Creative Director: David Saylor

CHAPTERS

DOG MAN

Behind the Epicness!

Yo, Homies, It's George and Harold again!

What up, dogs?

We're in 5th grade now, which means we're totally mature.

And deep!

I think I might grow a moustache!

Me too!

SQUEAK SQUEAK SQUEAK

AWESOME!

But... our deepness and maturishness comes with a high price tag.

Well **I** read it, and it inspired me to write a new DOG man novel!

It's a story of savagery...

... a tale of consequences...

...A Profound Look into the constructs of morality...

... And one ring to rule them all!

SLAP!

But First, a recap of our story thus far...

OUR STORY THUS FAR...
by George and Harold

One time there was a cop and a police dog...

...who got hurt in an explosion.

KA-BLAMMERS

When they got to the hospital, the doctor had sad news:

Boo Hoo

I'm sorry, but your body is dying.

And your head is dying, too, cop!!!

Rats!!!

But just when everything seemed hopeless, the nurse Lady got an idea.

Let's sew the dog's head onto the cop's body!

OK, nurse Lady!

So they did.

And soon, a new crime-fighting sensation was unleashed.

HOORAY FOR DOG MAN!

Along the way, Dog Man has made some very awesome friends.

Zuzu: World's Greatest Poodle

Sarah Hatoff: world's Greatest reporter

Chief: world's Greatest chief

our Hero

And one supa evil enemy!

WANTED
for being a jerk

PETEY
world's most evilest cat

Recently, Petey tried to clone himself...

I'll make a big, evil villain, just like me!

DNA   START

...but instead, he got a tiny, cute kitten who was nothing like him.

Papa!

Li'L Petey: world's Greatest kitty

Li'l Petey's Life started out sad...

Free Kitty

...but it wasn't sad for long.

DOG Man

Now Li'l Petey has a family.

Pat Pat Pat

Kiss Kiss Kiss

80-HD: world's Greatest Robot buddy

And that is a good place to start.

DOG Man

Tree-
House
CoMiX
Proudly
Presents

CHAPTER 1

A visit from
Kitty
Protective
Services

By George and Harold

One morning at Dog Man's house...

BUZZ
BUZZ
BUZZ

DOG MAN

clank
cLank
clank

...Li'L Petey and 80-HD were hard at work.

BUZZ
BUZZ
BUZZ

clank
clank
clank

Well, I'm all done reprogramming the Dogmobile!

Now it's Super easy to control!

How's the hydraulic Roof Ramp coming along?

CLAP CLAP

RRRR

RRR

RRRRRR

DOG MAN

AWESOME!!!

Dog Man

CLUNK!

I can't wait until Dog Man sees it!

Grand Ballroom

♪Ding

Good morning, Dog Man!!!

Look what me and 80-HD did!

We transformed the Grand Ballroom into the coolest clubhouse **EVER!!!**

Us three are going to be in a club, ok?

We'll call ourselves the **SUPA BuddieS!**

Most of the time, we'll just be our regular selves...

...But when danger rears its ugly head...

...We'll be super-heroes!!!

Look—I even made a cape for 80-HD!

And I made him a Flip-o-Rama mask!

FLIP FLOP FLIP

18

STEP 1.
First, Place your Left hand inside the dotted Lines marked "Left hand here." Hold The book open FLAT!

STEP 2:
Grasp the right-hand Page with your Thumb and index finger (inside the dotted Lines marked "Right Thumb Here").

STEP 3:
Now Quickly flip the right-hand page back and forth until the Picture appears to be Animated.

(for extra fun, try adding your own Sound-effects!)

O-RAMA

Remember,

while you are flipping,
be sure you can see
the image on page 23
AND the image on page 25.

If you flip quickly,
the two pictures will
start to look like
one **Animated** cartoon!

Don't forget to
add your own
sound-effects!

Left
hand here.

Right
Thumb
here.

I'll go to School...

...and we can play together when I get back, okay?

Bye, Dog Man! Bye, 80-HD!

Meanwhile... Well, hello there, little fella.

Hi, Papa!

Ha-Ha! I think you've confused me with someone else!

No I haven't!

I'm a kindly old social worker!!!

No you're not.

I only care about your best interests!!!

No you don't.

Look, kid, I'm NOT who you THINK I Am!

Yes you are!

Hey, where's the School at, Papa?

We're not going to School. We're getting outta town!

why?

Because you're in terrible **DANGER!**

why?

I'm not gonna tell you!

why?

Because every time I tell a story, you always interrupt me, like, a Thousand Times!

why?

BECAUSE You're A PEST!!!

why?

SiT DOWN!!!

why?

Because we need to talk!

why?

Look --- it's **very irritating** when you d

Hey Papa, you got weird hairs in your nose!

You Just INTERRU

I won't interrupt anymore. I'll be good.

ALright, because what I'm about to tell you is v

Hey Papa, is this story gonna be boring?

NO!

Okay. You may continue.

Well, it all started this morning when I was in

Hey Papa! Do y'wanna hear a joke?

I AM GOING TO FINISH TELLING MY STORY...

...AND YOU ARE GOING TO LISTEN QUIETLY WITH **NO** INTERRUPTIONS!!!

Okay.

CHAPTER 2
PETEY'S STORY
(WITH MANY (INTERRUPTIONS))

41

Sorry, Petey. The Judge says ya have to.

RATS!

So anyway...

Petey, meet Dr. Katz.

It's a pleasure to meet you, Petey.

Yeah, I know!

Hey Papa, that guy looks like the costume you wore.

JUST PAY ATTENTION!!! It'll all make sense soon!

OK.

SO ANYWAY...

ALRight! ALRight!

I guess it all started when I was a kitten.

I used to be in the Critter Scouts!

cs

Hey Papa, how come I'm wearing a hat?

That's NOT **YOU**! That's **ME** when I was a kitten!

Oh.

So anyway, I used to be an **AWESOME** scout!

SCOUT'S GUIDE TO GOOD BEHAVIOR

Here's another badge for you, Petey!

Sweeeet!

I was known far and wide for my good deeds and merit badges!

But it all ended one day when we went to play miniature golf.

PUTT PUTT ISLAND

But the water rose higher and higher...

... and soon we were washed away.

The storm raged for weeks and weeks.

Finally, we landed on a deserted island.

48

WHAT Are You Kids DoiNG?

I WAS GONE FoR TeN MinuTes...

...And You've ReGRessed into MANiACS!

What are You, a Bunch of ANiMALS??

When I find out who was responsible...

Petey did it!

Wait--- So that whole part about the Flood and the island was all make-believe?

Well, yeah---but that's not the point!

The point is, **I WAS BETRAYED!**

And then he started a **Fire!**

Then he fed my specs to the **SHARKS!**

We tried to **STOP** him!!!

JUST PAY ATTENTION!

Okay.

So Anyway...

...Then, we're gonna take over the world in our **GIANT ROBO-BRONTOSAURUS!!!**

It's Parked Outside!!!

HAW HAW HAW HAW HAW

HAW HAW HAW HAW HAW

64

65

So **THAT'S** why I came to get you...

...And **THAT'S** why we need to get as far away from here as possible.

But Papa, if the bad guys got locked up, why are we running?

Because they'll probably **ESCAPE**!

But how could they escape from a maximum security Prison?

Who knows? Maybe something **DUMB** will happen!

Tree-
House
Comix
Proudly
Presents

Chapter 3

SomeThing DumB HAPPenS!

by George Beard and Harold Hutchins

Meanwhile...

COPS

Ring-Ring

Hello?

Help! There's been a JaiL escape!!!

Where?

at the JaiL.

Oh!

I'll put my best man on it!!!!!!!

Oh, DOG MAN!

Dog Man is Late for work again, Chief!

Beep Beep Beep Beep Beep

DOG MAN! We Need your help!

Meet US AT The Jail in Ten Minutes!

AND DON'T Get Distracted!!!

Ten Minutes Later

Hello, I'm Sarah Hatoff reporting from Cat Jail...

...where Chief and Milly have just caught three crooks!

How'd ya do it?

Well, first they attacked us...

Let's roll the clip...

...IN FLIP-O-RAMA

Left hand here.

73

Right
Thumb
here.

Things were looking bad for us...

...So we ran to the Jail Library...

...and fought back using the **Power** of **BOOKS!**

Let's BOOK These Bozos!

Encyclopedia Obsoletica

Dictionary

OK, roll the clip!

FLIP-O-RAMA

Left hand here.

77

Right
Thumb
here.

I can't wait to show him what we did!!!

Here He comes now!!!

Oh boy, This is gonna be **GrEAT!**

cat Jail

NO--- WAIT!!

chief

NOOOO!

Come on, Zuzu! Let's follow them!

DOG MAN, Those Guys escaped because of **YOU!!!**

GO HOME!

But Chief—

Sorry, Milly. He's gotta Learn his Lesson!

...And **We've** gotta catch those crooks Again!

Tree-
House
Comix
Proudly
Presents

CHAPTER 4
Revenge OF The FLEAS!

by George and Harold

AAAAH!

Papa! You're s'posed to say "a big Robot brontosaurus who?"

This is Sarah Hatoff with a breaking news update!

A big Robot brontosaurus is attacking...

... and the good guys are in hot pursuit!

We should come up with a better name!

Yeah!

IT'S TOO LATE!!! I Already Ordered Coffee Mugs And Mouse Pads!!!

FLEAS

FLEAS

Besides --- We've got more **IMPORTANT** Things to do!!!

CHIEF

Not if we can help it!!!

CHIEF

FLIP-O-RAMA ★BATTLE★

CHIEF

Left hand here.

Right
Thumb
here.

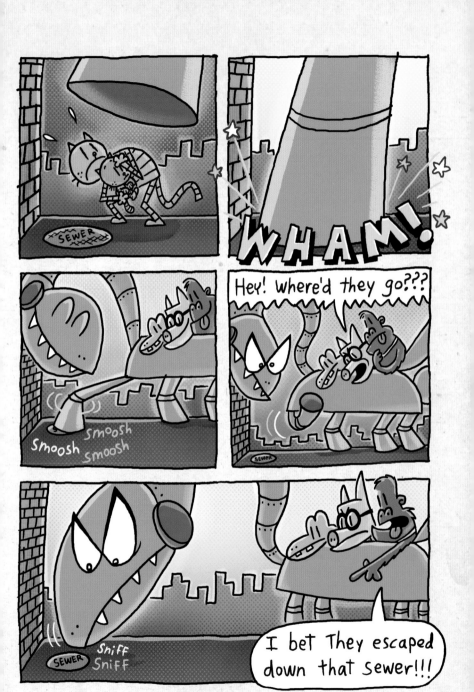

That's not the point!

The point is, you were expecting someone named "Dwayne."

But I switched it around!

That's why it's funny!

It woulda been funnier if the bathtub pooped on your head!

WHAT IS IT WITH YOU AND POOP?

Ha Ha Ha

CHAPTER 5
A Buncha Stuff That Happened Next

109

Meanwhile...

Where are we goin', Papa?

We've gotta get out of town! I told you!!!

No, Papa! We gotta go back and save Sarah and Zuzu and Milly and Chief!!!

We **CAN'T!** We don't have any weapons!

All we've got is this measly old Shrink ray! It only has **Two Shots** Left!!!

But Papa—

Besides, I'm the **BAD GUY!** Everybody knows that!!!

But Papa—

I make poor decisions! I'm a **SCOUNDREL!!!**

But Papa—

I can't be goin' around being all **Heroic** and stuff...

But Papa—

...I've got a **BAD REPUTATION** to uphold!!!

But Papa—

If you only knew the horrible things I've done...

...the awful, unforgivable things!!!

Meanwhile...

Petey --- Oh, Peeeetey!!!

Come out and Plaaay—aaay!!!

Come out, come out, wherever you are!

Alright, kid. Listen up!

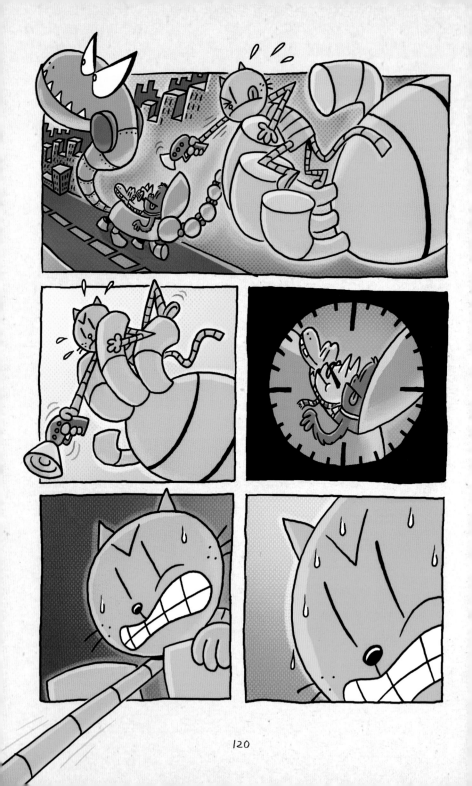

125

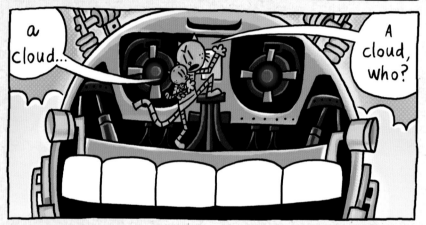

127

Oops. I mean, Hi, The Bark Knight!

Hi, 80-HD!

HEY!

I mean, Hi, Lightning Dude!!!

CRASH

You guys look awesome in your costumes!

I sure wish I hadn't forgotten **Mine!**

CHAPTER 6

SUPA BUDDIES

132

THAT'S NOT FUNNY!!!

ZAP

CRASH

Hey, you were right!

That **WAS** a funny story!

We're STILL FALLING!

And I'm about to crash into the ground!!!

PLOOF!

FLUP

Good catch, the Bark Knight!

But uh-oh!

We're about to crash into that factory!

Quick! Step on the brake!

SCREEECH

145

Don't celebrate just yet...

... 'CUZ WE'RE **BAAAAACK!!!**

It took forever, but we finally got ourselves out from under that building!!!

And **NOW**, we're gonna finish you **ALL** off...

...with **ONE ZAP** of our **killer death ray!**

YANK!

Looks like we're gonna have a Giant Robo-Battle...

...iN FLIP-O-RAMA!

Left hand here.

153

Right
Thumb
here.

Left hand here.

157

Right Thumb here.

Left hand here.

Right
Thumb
here.

That's my Papa!

I mean, that's Petey!

He's trying so hard to be good!

I always knew he had a good heart in there somewhere!

CHAPTER 7
THE DARKNESS

So I was thinking...

...Why are we fighting amongst **OURSELVES?**

If you and I set aside our differences...

...and we worked **TOGETHER...**

We'd be **UNSTOPPABLE!**

I mean, *REALLY...*

Think of the **FUN** we could have!!!

Think of the **CASH** we could swipe!

Think of the **POWER** we could wield!!!

Think of the **CHAOS** we could unleash!!!!!

Think of the **DARKNESS** we could inflict upon the unwashed masses!

Haven't you always wanted a sidekick?

A Partner in crime?

Isn't that why you Created that dumb Little kitten in the first place?

SWOOOSH

CRASH

Oh, NO!!! Petey's in trouble! Let's GO!!

Well, well, Well...

All of my **Enemies** Are together in **ONE PLACE!** How **CONVENIENT!!!**

OH, CRUNKY! OH, BUB!!!

CRUNKY! BUB!!!

178

If you catch one, you get good Luck!

I SAID I WASN'T TALKING TO YOU!

Hey, can you buy us a ice cream cone?

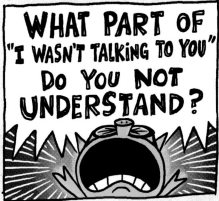

WHAT PART OF "I WASN'T TALKING TO YOU" DO YOU NOT UNDERSTAND?

Ummm...

...the middle Part?

182

I—I can't believe you guys saved me!

We're the good guys, Petey!

That's what we do!

But...

...Where's the kid?

WHERE'S Li'L PETEY?

I'm up here, playin' with the bad guys!

80-HD!!!

We gotta save Dog Man!!!

Oops! I mean, **Lightning Dude!!!**

We gotta save **The Bark Knight!!!**

189

DOG MAN---
WAKE UP!!!

The Bad guys
Are Coming!!!

Well, well, well...
What do we have
here?

It Looks like you guys got yourselves in a big **MESS!!!**

Do you have any **LAST WORDS** before we **ZAP** you all to SMiThereens?

Ummm...

...hmmm...

We'll tell ya our last word in a minute, ok?

Left
hand here.

Right
Thumb
here.

Left hand here.

Love, Sloppily

Right
Thumb
here.

Love, Sloppily

Hey Papa, Look!

Dog Man Kissed us!

Yeeeeeeeeah...

···Lovely.

HOORAY FOR DOG MAN! ···OOPS, WE MEAN The BARK Knight!

CHAPTER 8

MY DOG MAN HAS FLEAS!

But I'm a good guy now!!!

I know. But ya still gotta pay for the crimes ya did yesterday...

...and the day before that, and the day before that, and the...

WELL THAT'S JUST GREAT!!!

I WAS GOOD FOR, LIKE, THE WHOLE BOOK!

If you're happy, People just get **JeALOUS!**

Ya gotta be happy anyway, Papa!

You can spend **YeARS** creating stuff...

...Then a big robot brontosaurus can come along...

... and **ZAP** it all To **SMiThereeNS** in **TwO SeceNDS!!**

Ya gotta be creative anyway, Papa.

PETEY-YOU'RE BACK!

ka-click

chief

Hey kid, Y'wanna get some gelato with me after I escape tomorrow?

I don't know what gelato is, but okay!

Well, So Long, Petey!

chief

G'night, Chief!

Hey Chief, what's gelato?

It's like ice cream.

Oh.

sweeeet!

...if you thought our adventure was over...

Right now, George and Harold are busy reading **ANOther** old-fashioned book...

...getting **AWESOME NEW-FASHioNeD ideaS**...

... and desperately trying to figure out how to remove permanent marker from their faces before their moms find out!

So get ready for the next epic tale...

... of maturishness and deepality!!!

Because an all-new DOG MAN novel is coming!!!!

Tree-
HOUSE
CoMiX
Proudly
Presents

DOG MAN
BRAWL of the WILD

If You Like **THRILLS**...

...AND you Like **LAFFS**..

...AND You Like **AWESOMENESS**...

...Then **DOG MAN is GO!**

"Dog Man is GO?"

That don't make no sense!

BUT We Like it!!!

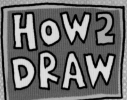

THE BARK KNIGHT

in **42** Ridiculously easy steps!

231

233

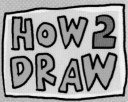

CAT KiD

in **41** Ridiculously easy steps!

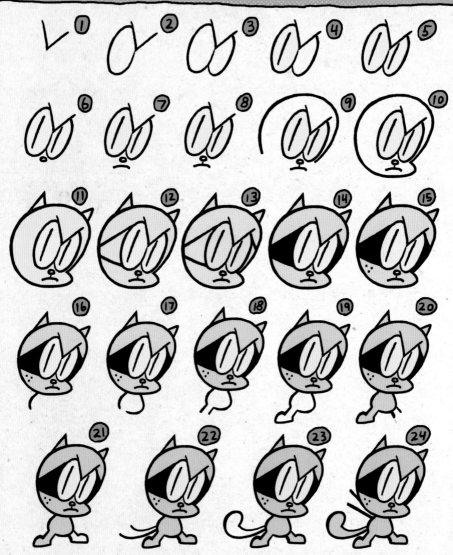

234

CRUNKY

in **26** Ridiculously easy steps!

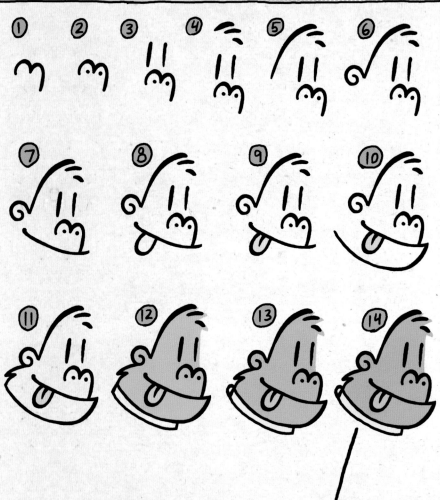

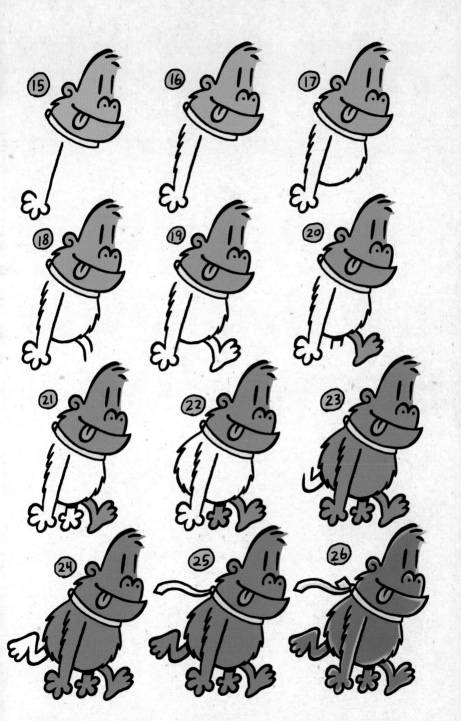

LiGHTNiNG DUDE LD

in **31** Ridiculously easy steps!

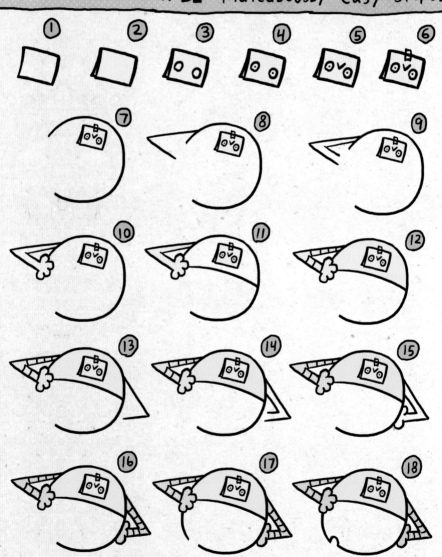

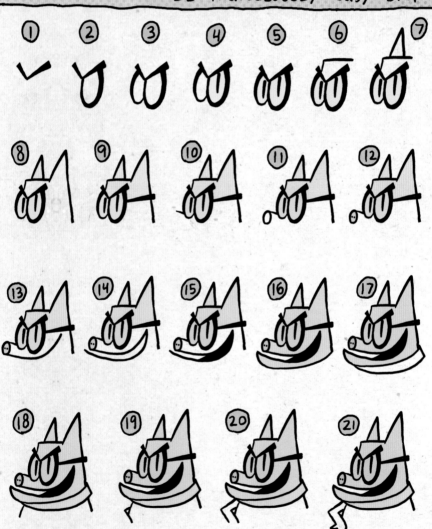

241

BUB

in **21** Ridiculously easy steps!

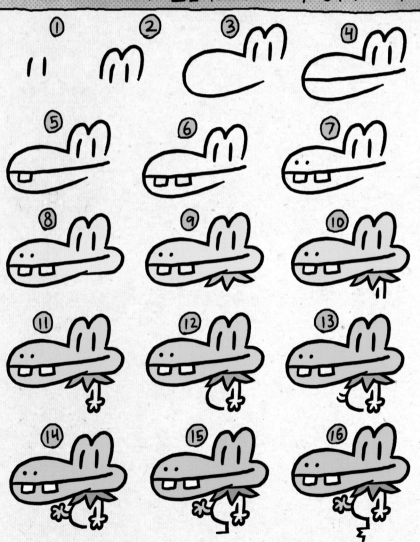

242

NOTES

by George and Harold

☆ Our favorite character from William Golding's <u>Lord of the Flies</u> is Piggy. The Piggy in our book is a bad guy, though.

☆ The dialogue on page 147 was inspired by quotes commonly attributed to Mark Twain and Dr. Seuss.

☆ The conversation on pages 220-221 was inspired by the poem "Anyway," by Kent M. Keith. A version of this poem is inscribed on the wall of Mother Teresa's home for Children in Calcutta, India.

☆ "I finally finished reading <u>Lord of the Flies</u>. It WAS awesome." — Harold Hutchins

ReAd to Your CAT, Kid!

The next day...

Jail Phone Rules:
1. Time Limit: 10 minutes.
2. No Hissing.
3. No chewing on cord.

Hey Kid— what's up???

I'm reading to my Dog, man!

Studies* show that Kids who read out loud to dogs...

...can improve their skills by up to 30%!

* University of California-Davis: Reading to Rover, 2010

BUT There's **MORE!**

Because **NOW,** There's a **NEW READING CRAZE** That's All the **RAGE!!!**

It's happening at animal shelters Everywhere!!!

ANIMAL SHELTER

Kids * can show up and reAd to Shelter cats!!!

The Kids get all of the great benefits from reading out loud to cats...

* accompanied by a parent or guardian

... and the cats get the benefits of human interaction and socialization.

This helps make it easier for shelter cats to get adopted!

It's a **Win·Win** for everybody!

Wow! That's a great idea, Papa!

CLICK

2 hours Later...

Cat Jail

Hey Petey! You've got a visitor!!!

I do?

Hey Kid. What'cha doing here?

I came to read To my cat, Kid!

Really?

check with
your local
animal shelter
and see if you
can volunteer to
READ TO YOUR
CAT, KID!

READING TO YOUR CAT IS ALWAYS A PAWS-ITIVE EXPERIENCE!

SOPHIE & SKIPPY

MAUDE & MAX

MAUDE & ABBY

MAX & ALEX

CHARLIE & PAPOOSA

#ReadtoyourcatKid

AARON & PAPOOSA

JAC, KATE & DELILAH

KOUME, RINKA & YUMA

SOPHIA, ISABELLE, SCOOT & NINJA

GALEN, FINN & RUCKUS

LEARN MORE AT PILKEY.COM!

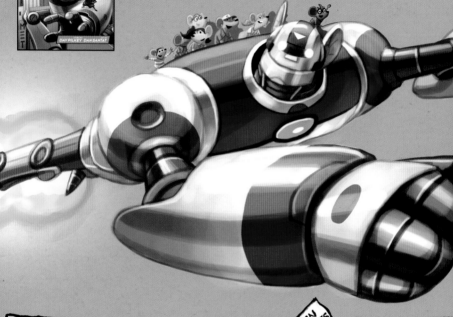

ABOUT THE AUTHOR-ILLUSTRATOR

When Dav Pilkey was a kid, he suffered from ADHD, dyslexia, and behavioral problems. Dav was so disruptive in class that his teachers made him sit out in the hall every day. Luckily, Dav loved to draw and make up stories. He spent his time in the hallway creating his own original comic books.

In the second grade, Dav Pilkey created a comic book about a superhero named Captain Underpants. His teacher ripped it up and told him he couldn't spend the rest of his life making silly books.

Fortunately, Dav was not a very good listener.

ABOUT THE COLORIST

Jose Garibaldi grew up on the South Side of Chicago. As a kid, he was a daydreamer and a doodler, and now it's his full-time job to do both. Jose is a professional illustrator, painter, and cartoonist who has created work for Dark Horse Comics, Disney, Nickelodeon, MAD Magazine, and many more. He lives in Los Angeles, California, with his wife and their cats.